# BOOK

Published by Ransom Publishing Ltd.
Radley House, 8 St. Cross Road, Winchester, Hampshire
SO23 9HX

www.ransom.co.uk

ISBN    978 184167 409 4
First published in 2013
Copyright © 2013 Ransom Publishing Ltd.

Illustrations copyright © 2013 The Comic Stripper Ltd.

# STEVE SHARP

## Gangster

by

### H. L. Dube

RANS♥M

## Steve Sharp

Steve was a cop. Now he works for himself. He is a hard man.

## Jaydeen

Jaydeen works for Steve. She is in love with Steve, but never tells him.

## Mrs Clayton

Mrs Clayton is rich. Her kid, Jo Clayton, is missing from home.

## Jo Clayton

Jo left home to shack up with Big John, a drug dealer.

## Big John

Big John makes big bucks selling drugs. He is a bad guy.

# ONE

I look in the mirror. It looks bad.

Big John did that. Big John, drug
pusher.

He smacked me between the eyes.

'Good tea, Jaydeen. Thanks.'

'Now tell me the story,' she says.

The girl I am looking for. Jo Clayton.

'She was in a club with Big John. He smacked me.'

So what next?' Jaydeen asks.

She knows I do not give up.

'I will find Jo – and Big John!'

# TWO

'A man wants to see you,' Jaydeen tells me. 'Frank the Hat.'

I walk to the door. No time to waste.

When Frank the Hat says go to his place, you go.

I walk to the Metro Club.

Guy on the door checks my I. D.

I go up some steps.

At the top of the steps I see a girl.

She's easy to look at.

My name is Sharp, Steve Sharp.

'Come in, Steve,' the girl says.

# THREE

Frank the Hat sits at a big desk.

He is a big guy. He is a rich man, but not a good guy.

Frank is a gangster.

'Sit down, Steve. Drink? Beer?'

'A glass of water, please,' I say.

Frank laughs.

He has bad teeth.

The girl does not laugh.

She looks at me. I know that look.

'This is Val Foster,' Frank says.

'Val. Meet Steve Sharp. A hard man who drinks water.'

I shake her hand.

Her hand is cool.

Val goes out to get a glass of water.

'You want to see me, Mr Frank?'

Everybody calls him Mr Frank.

'Yes. I want you to work for me, Steve.'

'I have a job, Mr Frank.'

'I pay good money, Steve. Big bucks to a hard man like you.'

Val Foster comes back with the water.

There is ice in the glass.

'Thanks, Mr Frank. But I work for myself.'

'I need a good man. To take good care of Val. I pay good money.'

Good money? I will look after this girl for nothing.

But I do not say this to Frank the Hat.

# FOUR

'So who gave you the black eyes?'
Frank asks.

'A guy called Big John. In the Doodle
Club.'

'Why did Big John smack you?'

'I touched the arm of his girl. So he put me to sleep.'

'A guy touches Val and I put *him* to sleep,' Frank says. 'And he never wakes up.'

'Big John is bad news,' I say.

'You want me to take him out?' Frank asks.

'No, Mr Frank. I will do that.'

'OK, Steve. You want to work for me, just tell me. OK?'

Frank tells Val to go with me to the front door.

'Sure, Frank,' she says.

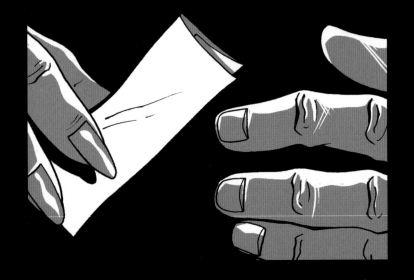

Out in the street, Val Foster touches
my arm.

'My mobile number,' she says. She
gives me a piece of paper.

'Call me, Steve!'

I am playing with fire. But I like this girl.

I like her a lot.

# STEVE SHARP

Now read
the next
Steve Sharp
book ....